MW00887531

PERFECT

PERFECT

DR. FRANK STILE

Illustrations by Miki Funderburk
Audio version read by Darryl Gilley

Palmetto Publishing Group
Charleston, SC

Perfect
Copyright © 2019 by Dr. Frank Stile
All rights reserved

First Edition

Printed in the United States

Hardcover ISBN-13: 978-1-64111-395-3
Paperback ISBN-13: 978-1-64111-476-9
eBook ISBN-13: 978-1-64111-477-6

Dedication

To Selena Philips without whom this story would never have been told.

And to Antoine de Saint-Exupery because, like him "I don't want this book to be taken lightly - telling these memories is so painful for me".

And of course Anthony Robbins who woke me up so many years ago.

He has got **PERFECT** skin

So smooth and tight

PERFECT teeth

So straight and white

He's got a **PERFECT** house

And the **PERFECT** wife

His **PERFECT** neighbors think

He's got the **PERFECT** life

He always says **PERFECT** things

At just the **PERFECT** time

He eats at **PERFECT** restaurants

And always chooses the **PERFECT** wine

He has the most **PERFECT** parties

Where he shares his **PERFECT** thoughts

He stands with **PERFECT** posture

Displaying the **PERFECT** things he bought

His friends are all **PERFECT** too

They're quite fashionable at that

And all are **PERFECTLY** fit

Not one of them is fat

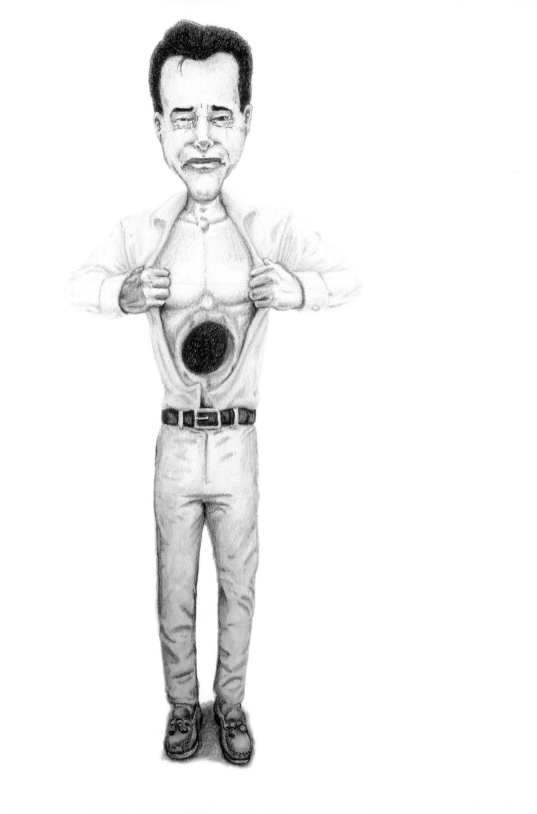

But there is a **PERFECT** emptiness

A hollowness he feels

A profound sadness

He struggles to conceal

He has a sense of incompleteness

Though he does not appear to care

And growing deep within him

Is a feeling of quiet despair

Maybe it's the most **PERFECT** feeling

Which only LOVE can give

That can fill this **PERFECT** void

With which he's had to live

In our very imperfect world

True **PERFECTION** is rarely seen

Though you may find it if you look hard enough

Up and down and in between

Perhaps **PERFECTION** is a feeling

Or maybe it's just a state of mind

Is it something you get from sharing

Or simply being kind

PERFECTION is achieved

Through generous acts

Not from the purchases you've made

Or the recounting of meaningless facts

Until he accepts this simple truth

He'll continue on his way

Living his **PERFECT** life

In self-deception day after day

Soon his **PERFECT** life will be over

And He'll finally get to rest

His funeral will be **PERFECT** too

Attended by the best

They'll place his **PERFECT** body

In a most **PERFECT** box

Tightly shut the lid

Securing all the locks

Then they'll place his **PERFECT** remains

Body **PERFECTLY** whole

Exactly six feet down

Into a **PERFECTLY** square hole

Many will attend his funeral

They will all have **PERFECT** frowns

And when his most **PERFECT** ceremony is over

They'll leave his **PERFECT** town

They'll return to their **PERFECT** homes

And as they turn in for the night

They'll lay their heads on **PERFECT** pillows

And turn off their **PERFECT** lights

Occasionally some may think of him

And all the **PERFECT** things he's done

Sometimes with envy

Believing it was all such **PERFECT** fun

And if you listen carefully

As they speak their last good-nights

They'll say "He surely had it all...

Boy, he had the most **PERFECT** life!"

THE END